The Great LOVE SONGS Of The 50s

C000176428

All I Have To Do Is Dream The Everly Brothers **3**

All The Way Frank Sinatra **6**

Blueberry Hill Fats Domino **9**

Don't Elvis Presley **12**

Everyday Buddy Holly **15**

Fever Peggy Lee **20**

From Here To Eternity Frank Sinatra **24**

Hallelujah I Love Her So Ray Charles **34**

I Walk The Line Johnny Cash **27**

Love Me Tender Elvis Presley **40**

Magic Moments Perry Como **42**

Memories Are Made Of This Dean Martin **45**

Misty Johnny Mathis **48**

No Other Love Ronnie Hilton **52**

Puppy Love Paul Anka **56**

Put Your Head On My Shoulder Paul Anka **60**

Sea Of Love Phil Phillips & The Twilights **70**

Smoke Gets In Your Eyes The Platters **67**

The Song From Moulin Rouge (Where Is Your Heart)
The Percy Faith Orchestra featuring Felicia Sanders **74**

Take Me To Your Heart Again (La Vie En Rose) Édith Piaf **77**

Tears On My Pillow Little Anthony & The Imperials **82**

A Teenager In Love Dion & The Belmonts **86**

That's Amoré Dean Martin **90**

The Twelfth Of Never Johnny Mathis **96**

You Don't Know Me Jerry Vale **100**

Young Love Tab Hunter **106**

Your Cheatin' Heart Hank Williams **109**

Wise Publications
part of The Music Sales Group
London/New York/Paris/Sydney/Copenhagen/Berlin/Madrid/Tokyo

Published by

Wise Publications
14-15 Berners Street, London W1T 3LJ, UK.

Exclusive Distributors:

Music Sales Limited
Distribution Centre, Newmarket Road,
Bury St Edmunds, Suffolk IP33 3YB, UK.

Music Sales Pty Limited
120 Rothschild Avenue, Rosebery,
NSW 2018, Australia.

Order No. AM986777
ISBN 1-84609-706-1
This book © Copyright 2006 Wise Publications,
a division of Music Sales Limited.

Front cover photo courtesy of Jupiter Images.
Back cover photographs courtesy of LFI.

Printed in the EU.

www.musicsales.com

All I Have To Do Is Dream

Words & Music by Boudleaux Bryant

-ev - er I want you___ all I have to do is dream,_____ dream, dream, dream. 2. When
-ev - er I want you___ all I have to do is

dream._____

I can make you mine,

taste your lips of wine, a - ny - time, night or day.

On - ly trou - ble is, gee whiz, I'm dream-ing my life___ a

- way!_____ I   need   you   so   that I could die,   I   love   you   so

and that is why   when - ev - er   I   want   you___   all   I   have   to   do   is

dream._____

dream._____

Dream,   dream,   dream,_   dream,_____   dream,   dream,   dream,_   dream.

All The Way

Words by Sammy Cahn
Music by James Van Heusen

Tall - er_____ than the tall - est tree is, that's how it's got to feel; deep - er_____ than the deep blue sea is, that's how deep it goes,— if it's real. When some - bo - dy needs you, it's no good un - less she needs you all the way.

Blueberry Hill

Words & Music by Larry Stock, Al Lewis & Vincent Rose

still _____ on Blue - ber - ry Hill _____

_____ and lin - gered un - til _____ my dreams came

true. _____ The wind in the wil - low played _____

_____ love's sweet mel - o - dy; _____ but all of those

11

Don't

Words & Music by Jerry Leiber & Mike Stoller

Everyday

Words & Music by Charles Hardin & Norman Petty

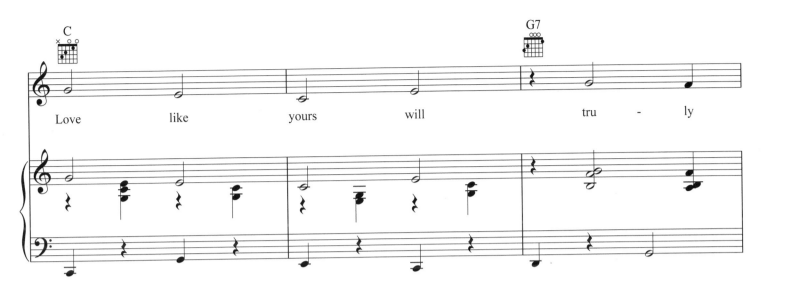

Love   like   yours   will   tru - ly

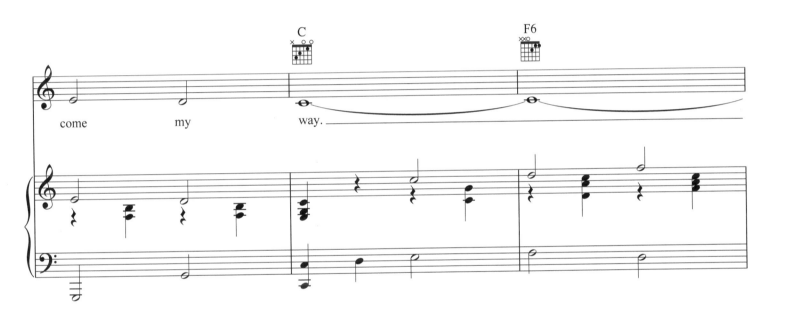

come   my   way. _____

Fever

Words & Music by John Davenport & Eddie Cooley

Moderate Jump beat

1. Nev-er know how much I love you, Nev-er know how much I
2. Sun lights up the day-time, Moon lights up the

care. When you put your arms a-round me, I get a
night. I light up when you call my name, And you

fe - ver that's so hard_____ to bear.
know I'm gon - na treat_____ you right. You give me fe - ver

When you kiss me, fe - ver when you hold_____ me

tight. Fe - ver in the morn - ing,

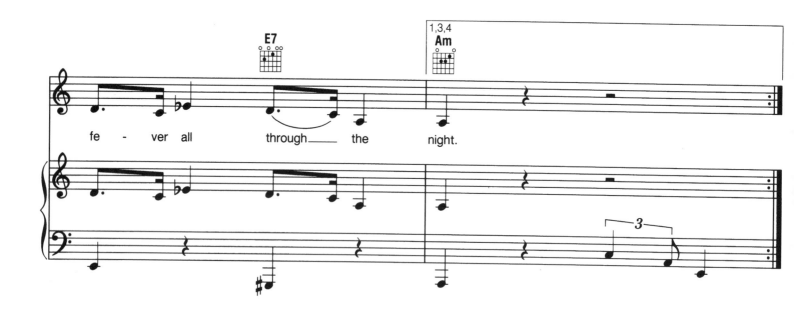

fe - ver all through___ the night.

night. Ev - 'ry-bod - y's got the fe - ver, that is some - thing

you all know. Fe - ver is - n't such a new thing,

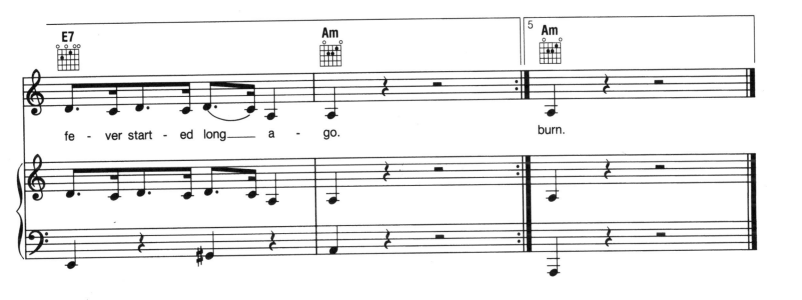

fe - ver start - ed long___ a - go.   burn.

Verse 3 Romeo loved Juliet
        Juliet she felt the same,
        When he put his arms around her, he said,
        "Julie, baby you're my flame."

Chorus Thou givest fever, when we kisseth
        Fever with my flaming youth,
        Fever – I'm afire
        Fever, yea I burn forsooth.

Verse 4 Captain Smith and Pocahantas
        Had a very mad affair,
        When her Daddy tried to kill him, she said,
        "Daddy-o don't you dare."

Chorus Give me fever, with his kisses,
        Fever when he holds me tight.
        Fever – I'm his Missus
        Oh Daddy won't you treat him right.

Verse 5 Now you've listened to my story
        Here's the point that I have made:
        Chicks were born to give you fever
        Be it fahrenheit or centigrade.

Chorus They give you fever when you kiss them,
        Fever if you live and learn.
        Fever – till you sizzle
        What a lovely way to burn.

23

From Here To Eternity

Words by Robert Wells
Music by Fred Karger

I Walk The Line

Words & Music by Johnny Cash

Mmm.

1. I keep a

close watch on this heart of mine. I keep my

eyes wide op - en all the time. I keep the

ends out for the tie that binds, be - cause you're

mine, I walk the line.

Mmm.

2. I find it
4. You've got a

ve - ry, ve - ry ea - sy to be true.
way to keep me on your side.

I find my -
You give me

- self a - lone when each day is through.
cause for love that I can't hide.

Yes I'll ad -
For you I

- mit that I'm ____ a fool for you,
know I'd ev - en try to turn the tide,

be - cause you're
be - cause you're

To Coda ⊕

mine, I walk the line.
mine, I walk the line.

Mmm.

3. As sure as

night is dark and day is light. I keep you

on my mind both day and night. And hap - pi -

D.S. al Coda

Coda

close watch on this heart of mine. I keep my

eyes wide op - en all the time. I keep the

ends out for the tie that binds, be - cause you're

mine, I walk the line. Mmm.

Repeat to fade

Hallelujah I Love Her So

Words & Music by Ray Charles

Let me tell you 'bout a girl I know,— she is my ba-by and she

Love Me Tender

Words & Music by Elvis Presley & Vera Matson

Magic Moments

Words by Hal David
Music by Burt Bacharach

Mag - ic mo - ments, mem - 'ries we've been

shar - ing. Mag - ic mo - ments,

when two hearts are car - ing. Time can't e -

rase the mem - 'ry of these mag - ic

mo - ments filled with love.

filled with love. _____

Memories Are Made Of This

Words & Music by Terry Gilkyson, Richard Dehr & Frank Miller

Don't for - get a small moon - beam___
With some bless-ings from a - bove___

Fold in light-ly with a dream.
Serve it gen-'rous-ly with love.___

Your lips and mine, Two sips of wine, Mem - or -
One man, and one wife, One love thro' life, Mem - or -

To Coda

ies are made of this.___
ies are made of this.___
Then add the

46

Misty

Words & Music by Erroll Garner & Johnny Burke

Slowly, with expression

misty, the mo - ment you're near. You can say that you're

lead - ing me on,_____ but it's just what I

want you to do.____ Don't you no - tice how

hope - less - ly I'm lost,____ that's why I'm fol - low - ing you.

51

No Other Love

Words by Oscar Hammerstein II
Music by Richard Rodgers

Puppy Love

Words & Music by Paul Anka

Put Your Head On My Shoulder

Words & Music by Paul Anka

love me too._____

Some peo-ple say_____ that love's a game,_____

Smoke Gets In Your Eyes

Words by Otto Harbach
Music by Jerome Kern

nied. _____ They said some - day you'll

find, all who love are blind, _____ when your heart's on

fire, you must re - a - lize smoke gets in your eyes. _____

accel.

a tempo

Un poco piu mosso

So I chaffed _ them and I gay - ly laughed _ to think they could doubt my

mf

68

love.   Yet to-day ___ my love has   flown a-way, ___   I am with -

out   my   love.   Now   laugh-ing friends de-

ride,   tears I can-not   hide, _____   so I smile and

say,   "When a love-ly flame dies,   smoke gets in your   eyes." ___

Sea Of Love

Words & Music by George Khoury & Philip Bastiste

The Song From Moulin Rouge
(Where Is Your Heart)

Words by William Engvick
Music by Georges Auric

eyes, pre - tend-ing that I'm some - one else? You

must break the spell, this cloud that I'm

un - der. So please won't you tell, dar - ling,

where is your heart? When - heart? _____

dim. e rall.

Take Me To Your Heart Again
(La Vie En Rose)

Words by Edith Piaf
Music by R.S. Louiguy

Tears On My Pillow

Words & Music by Sylvester Bradford & Al Lewis

pain___ in my heart___ caused___ by you.___ Hoo hoo hoo hoo hoo.

Love is not a gad-get, _____ love is not a toy.

When you find the one you love {she'll/he'll} fill your heart___ with joy.

Be-fore you go a-way,___ my dar-ling, think of me.___

A Teenager In Love

Words & Music by Doc Pomus & Mort Shuman

1. Each time we have a quar-rel it al-most
(Verse 2 see block lyric)

breaks my heart, 'cause I am so a-fraid

you. I'll be a lone - ly one if

you should say we're through. If you want to

make me cry, that won't be so hard to do.

And if you should say good - bye, I'll still go on lov - ing you.

Verse 2:
One day I feel so happy
Next day I feel so sad.
I guess I'll learn to take
The good with the bad.

Each night I ask the stars above
Why must I be a teenager in love?

89

That's Amoré

Words & Music by Harry Warren & Jack Brooks

In Na - po - li, _____ where love is king, _____ when boy meets

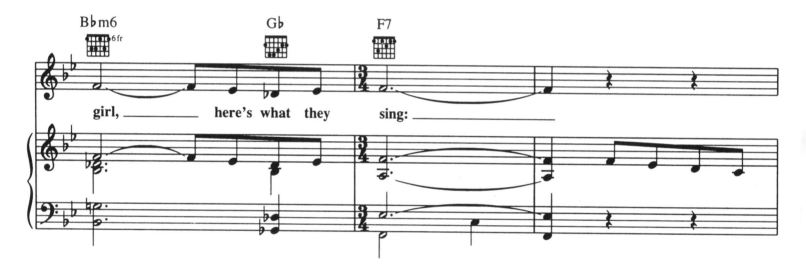

girl, _____ here's what they sing: _____

When the

90

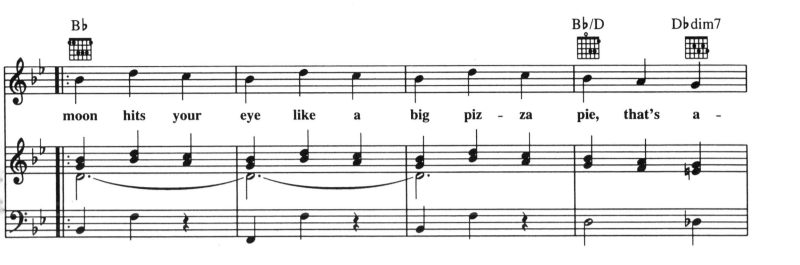

moon hits your eye like a big piz - za pie, that's a -

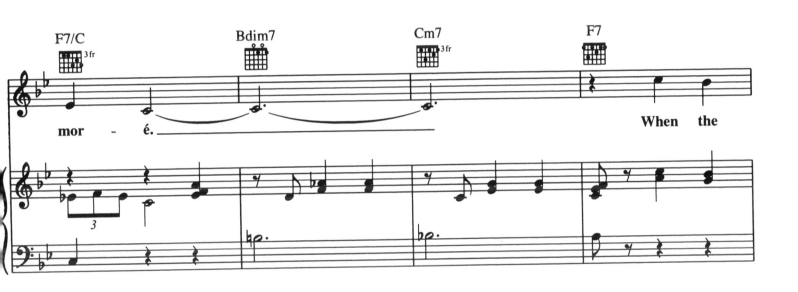

mor - é. When the

world seems to shine like you've had too much wine, that's a -

mor - é. _____ Bells will

ring, ting - a - ling - a - ling, ting - a - ling - a - ling, and you'll sing, "Vee - ta

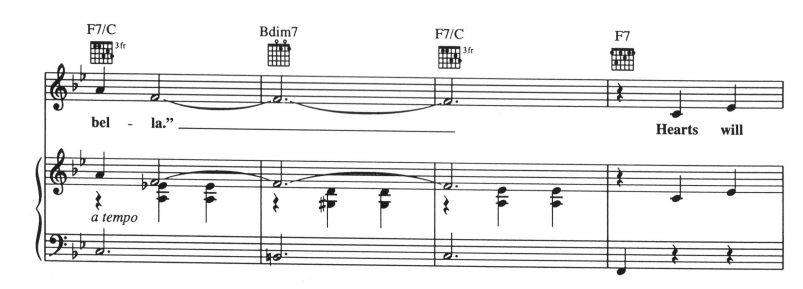

bel - la." _____ Hearts will

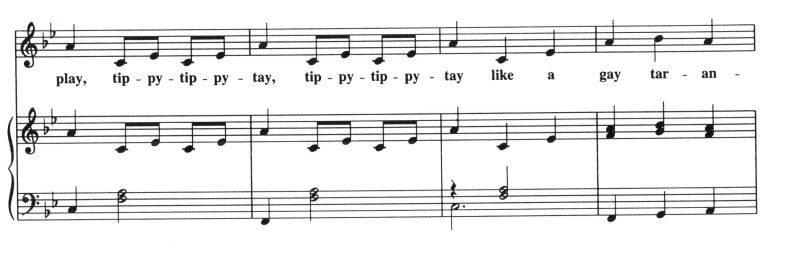

play, tip - py - tip - py - tay, tip - py - tip - py - tay like a gay tar - an -

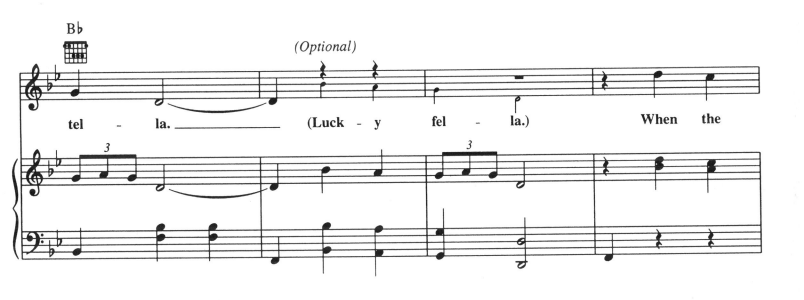

Bb

(Optional)

tel - la. _____ (Luck - y fel - la.) When the

Bb/D **Db dim7**

stars make you drool just like pas - ta fa - zool, that's a -

The Twelfth Of Never

Words by Paul Francis Webster
Music by Jerry Livingston

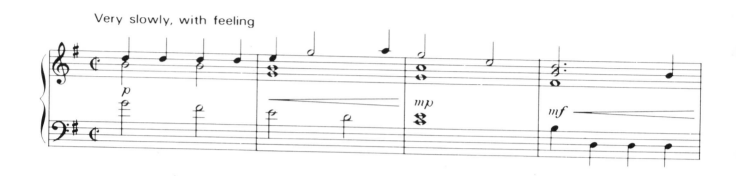

You Don't Know Me

Words & Music by Cindy Walker & Eddy Arnold

Young Love

Words & Music by Carol Joyner & Ric Cartey

mine._____ The hea - ven - ly touch of your em - brace tells

me no one can take your place ev - - - - -

- er_____ in my heart._____ Young

love, first love,_____ filled with

Verse 2:
Just one kiss from your sweet lips
Will tell me that your love is real
And I can feel that it's true.
We will vow to one another
There will never be another love
For you or for me.

Your Cheatin' Heart

Words & Music by Hank Williams

110